The empty pot

GW00659749

Story written by Abbie Rushton
Illustrated by Tim Archbold

Speed Sounds

Consonants   *Ask children to say the sounds.*

f	l	m	n	r	s	v	z	sh	th	ng
ff	ll	mm	nn	rr	ss	ve	zz			nk
ph	(le)	mb	kn	wr	se		se			
			gn		(c)		s			
					(ce)					

b	c	d	g	h	j	p	qu	t	w	x	y	ch
bb	k	dd	gg		g	(pp)		tt	wh			tch
	ck		gu		ge							
					dge							

Each box contains one sound but sometimes more than one grapheme.
*Focus graphemes for this story are **circled**.*

Vowels

Ask children to say the sounds in and out of order.

a	e ea	i	o	u	ay a͡-e a ai aigh	ee ea e y	igh i͡-e ie i y	(ow) (o-e) (oa) (o) oe

oo u͡-e ue ew	oo	ar	or oor ore aw	air are	ir ur er	ou ow	oy oi	ire	ear

Story Green Words

found   spoke   wise   oak   thrown   case   friends*

Ask children to say the syllables and then read the whole word.

Chi|na   em|per|or   pa|lace   sha|dow   a|lone   seed|ling

ex|cept   so|rrow   i|dea   hon|est*

Ask children to read the root first and then the whole word with the suffix.

grow → growing   boast → boasted   green → greenest

health → healthy   sow → sowed   hobble → hobbled

groan → groaned   emerald → emeralds

* Challenge Words

6

Vocabulary Check

Discuss the meaning (as used in the story) after the children have read each word.

	definition:	sentence:
boasted	showed off	Bo boasted, "My seed will grow to be as strong as the tallest tree."
sowed	planted	Then he sowed the seed.
seedling	a very young plant growing from a seed	... Bo showed Jun his little green seedling.
sorrow	unhappiness	He was filled with sorrow.
despair	feeling sad and worried	Jun was thrown into despair.
hobbled	walked with difficulty	The emperor hobbled past...

Red Words

were	by	one	bought
here	above	there	tall
all	who	mother	water
old	their	come	father
put	my	here	two

The empty pot

Long ago in China, there was a wise old emperor.
"I'm growing old," said the emperor, "and I have no child to take my place when I die."
Night after night he lay awake thinking about this.
Then one morning, he had an idea.

"I shall hold a contest," the emperor said. "The child who can grow the strongest and greenest plant will become the next emperor!"

Children from across the land rushed to the palace for the contest.
Each child was given a tiny seed to take home and grow.

Jun went with his friends, Bo and Han.

Bo boasted: "My seed will grow to be as strong as
the tallest tree."
Han boasted: "My seed will grow
to be as green as the
emperor's emeralds."

Jun was quiet.

When Jun got home, he found a perfect pot. He put stones in the bottom and filled it with dark, rich soil. Then he sowed the seed.

Every day, Jun watered his seed. Every day, he checked it. But no little green shoot popped up.

Two weeks later, Bo showed Jun his little green seedling. "Look!" he boasted. "It's starting to grow. I shall be the emperor!"

Han ran over. "Mine is starting to grow too!" he boasted. "*I* shall be the emperor."

Jun looked at his own empty pot. He was filled with sorrow.
"What am I doing wrong?" he cried to his mother.
"Don't give up," Jun's mother replied.

Jun tried everything. He put his pot in the shadow of an old
oak tree, in case his little seed wanted less light. He put it in
the window, in case it wanted more light. He sat and spoke
to it, in case it didn't like to be alone.

But still there was no little shoot.

Jun was thrown into despair. "How can I take an empty pot to the emperor?" he groaned.

"You must go," Jun's mother said. "Tell him what happened. You did your best."

So Jun took his empty pot to the palace and Bo and Han took their strong, healthy plants.

The emperor hobbled past the rows of children.

Suddenly, he stopped. "What happened here?" he asked, looking into Jun's pot.

Jun looked at the ground. "I did my best," he mumbled in a low voice. "But my seed did not grow."

The emperor looked around and everyone waited.

"It seems that this boy is the only honest child here," the emperor said.
"You were all given seeds that were roasted."

"Roasted?" said Jun, confused.
"But a cooked seed cannot grow!"
"Exactly!" said the emperor.
"All you children tried to cheat
by planting different seeds.
All except one."

Then he looked at Jun and smiled.
He had found a good and wise child
to become the next emperor.

Questions to talk about

Ask children to TTYP each question using 'Fastest finger' (FF) or 'Have a think' (HaT).

p.10   (FF)   Who did Jun go to the palace with?

pp.11–12 (HaT) How did Jun feel when he saw Bo and Han's seedlings?

p.12   (FF)   What did Jun do to try to get his seed to grow?

p.13   (FF)   What advice did Jun's mother give him?

p.14   (HaT) Why did Jun look at the ground and speak quietly?

p.15   (HaT) Were you surprised by the emperor's reaction to Jun's empty pot? Why?

p.15   (HaT) Why did the emperor choose Jun to be the next emperor?

Questions to read and answer

(Children complete without your help.)

1. The emperor was growing **old / taller / bored**.

2. The emperor held a **race / party / contest** to choose the next emperor.

3. Jun sowed his seed **in the ground / in a pot / in a bucket**.

4. Jun took his **little shoot / strong, healthy plant / empty pot** to the palace.

5. The emperor said the seeds had been **eaten / roasted / lost**.

Speedy Green Words

Ask children to practise reading the words across the rows, down the columns and in and out of order clearly and quickly.

about	home	dark	low
lay	empty	window	day
tried	long	only	each
tiny	take	boy	stones
light	own	green	awake